Open Windows

A Beka Book Publications
a ministry of *Pensacola Christian College*
Box 18000, Pensacola, Florida 32523

Open

Windows

ULLIN W. LEAVELL

MARY LOUISE FRIEBELE

Open Windows

Golden Rule Series

ULLIN W. LEAVELL
Formerly Professor of Education and Director of McGuffey Reading Clinic, University of Virginia, Charlottesville, Va.

MARY LOUISE FRIEBELE
Professional Writer for Children, Clearwater, Florida

Sponsored by The Palmer Foundation, Texarkana, Arkansas-Texas

———————— 1986 Edition ————————

1994 Printing C90

Acknowledgments

Highlights for Children, "Because I'm Happy" by Edna Hull Miller, copyright 1954, by permission of *Highlights for Children*, Columbus, Ohio.

Humpty Dumpty's Magazine, "The King Who Could Not Smile" by Hazel M. Kulik, copyright 1955.

Jack and Jill, "The Other Way Around," adapted from "The Wisdom of the Lord," copyright 1955 by The Curtis Publishing Company.

The artists who drew the pictures in this book are:

Cover by Irene Haas

Sheilah Beckett, pp. 181–185

Mel Crawford, pp. 129, 137–142, 151–156

Dick Dodge, pp. 37–43, 45–50, 52–57, 59–64

John Ferni, pp. 67–73, 75–80, 82–87, 89–93

Irene Haas, pp. 1–3, 159–165, 167–172, 174–179

William Hutchinson, pp. 97–103, 105–110, 112–117

Joe and Beth Krush, pp. 5–13, 15–20, 22–27, 29–34, 127

James Ponter, pp. 120–125

Ed Vebell, pp. 130–135, 144–149

Stories in This Book

At Play

At School

At Home

At Work

At Party Time

At Story Time

The Circus

"I want to play circus," said Jack.
"Do you want to play circus
with me, Susan?"

"Oh, yes!" said Susan.
"We can all do something funny."

"You can do something funny,"
said Jack.
"I want to run the circus."

Then Susan and Jack
went to see Tommy.

Jack said, "Tommy, we want
to play circus."
Do you want to play, too?"

"Oh, yes!" said Tommy.
"And look what I have!
You and Susan can do
something funny.
I will run
the circus."

"No, Tommy," said Jack.
"I am the man
who runs the circus."

"Oh, Jack!" said Susan.
"I like Tommy's funny hat.
It is a good hat for a circus man.
Do you have a big hat like Tommy's?"

Jack said, "No, I do not have
a hat like Tommy's.
But if Tommy gets to run the circus,
I will not play."

Susan looked at Tommy,
and Tommy looked at Susan.
Then Susan said, "Look, Jack.
If you do not want to play,
no one is going to make you!"
And she went home to get
something funny for the circus.

Jack went home, too.
He said, "Mother,
I do not think
I want to play circus.
"I will not have fun
if I am not the man
who runs the circus."

"But, Jack!"
said Mother.
"What fun can you have
if you are not
in the circus at all?"

"No fun at all!" said Jack.
"I did not think of that!"
Then he said, "Mother,
I do want to play circus.
Can you think of something funny
that I can do?"

All the boys and girls laughed
when Jack came out to play.

"Oh, Jack!" said Susan.
"You do look funny!"

"Now we all have something good
to do in the circus," said Tommy.
"Now we can ALL have fun!"

What Did Jack Want?

    1. Did Jack
want to be this?

2. Did Jack
want to be this?

3. What did Jack get to be?

What Did Tommy Have?

    1. Did Tommy have something
that Jack did not have?

    2. What was it?

    3. Did it help Tommy
get what he wanted?

Was Jack Happy?

    1. Was Jack happy when he said,
"I will not play circus"?

    2. Was Jack happy
when he did play circus?

The Blue and Yellow Boats

"Look, Jack!" said Tommy.
"Look at my blue boat.
Look at it go!"

"Yes," said Jack.
"You have a fast boat, Tommy.
But look at my yellow boat.
My boat can go fast, too."

But Jack's boat did not go fast
like Tommy's.
It did not go fast at all.

Tommy laughed.
"Look, Jack!" he said.
"Look at my blue boat.
That boat of yours
will not go fast like my boat.
I win! I win!"

"Yes, Tommy," said Jack.
"You win."

Then Jack said, "No boat
can go fast all the time, Tommy.
My boat did not go fast that time,
but it can."

"I do not think it can," said Tommy.
"Do you want to try it now?"

"Yes," said Jack. "I do."

Away went Tommy's little blue boat,
and away went the yellow boat, too.
But Jack's boat did not go fast at all.
"I win!" said Tommy.
"I win again."

Then they ran to get the boats.
"See," said Tommy.
"That boat of yours
can't go fast like my boat."

Jack looked at the yellow boat.
He looked at Tommy's blue boat.
"Yes, I see that now," said Jack.
"But I think I see what I can do
to make my boat go fast."

Then Jack ran home.
"Father, will you help me make
my boat look like Tommy's?" he said.
"Tommy's boat looks like this."

"Your boat will not go fast
like Tommy's, will it?" said Father.

"No," said Jack.
"But now I know what I have to do.
Tommy will have a big surprise
when I try my boat again."

Tommy and Jack went to play
with the boats again.

"I think my boat will surprise you
this time," said Jack.

Away went Tommy's little blue boat,
and away went the yellow boat, too.
But this time Tommy's boat
was not as fast as Jack's.

"Oh, boy!" said Jack.
"It did help to try again!
This time I win!"

Why Did Tommy's Boat Win?

    1. Did Tommy's boat look like this?

    2. Did it look like this?

Why Did Jack's Boat Win?

    1. Did it win
when it looked like this?

    2. Did it win
when it looked like this?

Why Did Jack Win?

    1. Did he stop trying?
    2. Did he try and try again?

The Dime

Tommy saw it on the street,
and he ran to get it.
Then he looked up the street
and down, but there was no one there.

"Oh, boy!" said Tommy.
"This is my dime now!"

"What can I get
with this dime?"
said Tommy.
"I can get a new ball.
I can go for a pony ride.
I can get a toy airplane
like Jack's."

Then Tommy laughed.
"I know!" he said.
"Candy is what I want!
I will get candy with my dime."

Then Tommy saw Betsy and Jack
run out of Betsy's house.

"Tommy!" said Jack.
"Betsy has lost a dime.
We have looked in the house,
but we can't find it there."

"I may have lost it out here,"
said Betsy.
"Will you help look for it, Tommy?"

Tommy did not look up.
"Where do you think you lost it?"
he said.

Betsy said, "This is where
I had it when I said good-by
to my father."

"Oh, Betsy!" said Tommy.
"You will get a new dime
when he finds out you lost that one."

"No," said Betsy.
"I had to work for that dime.
I had to help Mother in the house.
Oh, Tommy, help me look for it!"

Then Jack ran up to Betsy.
"I can't find your dime," he said.
"I have looked all around here."

Tommy looked down at the street.
How he wanted that dime!
He wanted a new ball.
He wanted a pony ride.
He wanted candy.
But the dime was Betsy's.

"Here, Betsy," said Tommy.
"Here is your dime."

How happy Betsy was!
"Oh, thank you!" she said.
"I know what I will get
with this dime."

"What?" said Tommy. "A pony ride?"
"What?" said Jack. "A new doll?"

"No," laughed Betsy.
"We all had to work for this dime.
I think I will get some candy.
Then we can all have some!"

Who Had Lost Something?

1. Had Tommy lost something?
2. Had Betsy lost something?
3. Had Jack lost something?

What Was Lost?

1. Was it a time?
2. Was it a dime?

Who Wanted It?

1. Did Tommy want the dime?
2. Did Jack want it?
3. Did Betsy want it?

What Can You Get with a Dime?

1. Can you get a pony?
2. Can you get a ride on a pony?
3. Can you get a toy airplane?
4. Can you get a ride on a big airplane?

What Did Betsy Get with the Dime?

1. Did she get some candy?
2. Why did Tommy get some candy, too?
3. Why did Jack get some candy, too?

A FUNNY SLED

There was snow on the houses.
There was snow on the streets.
Up and down and all around
there was new white snow.

But Susan was not happy.
With all that snow to play on,
Susan did not have a sled.

"Oh, Mother!" said Susan.
"I do want a sled!
I want to go for a ride
on that new white snow."

"You can use this box
for a sled," said Mother.
"Do you want to try it, Susan?"

"That box!" said Susan.
"I can't use a box for a sled!
The boys and girls
will make fun of me, Mother."

"I know what!" said Mother.
"Here is a tray
that will make a good sled.
Run out and see if it works."

"No, thank you," said Susan.
"The boys and girls
will make fun of me, Mother.
No one uses a tray for a sled."

Then Jack came and wanted Susan
to come out and play.

"I can't go," said Susan.
"I have no sled."

"Can't your mother find something
that you could use?" said Jack.

"I said she could use this tray
if she wanted to," said Susan's mother.
"But she thinks the boys and girls
will laugh at her."

"Oh, boy!" said Jack.
"Could I try it?"

Susan's mother laughed.
"Some girls do not know
how to have fun, do they?" she said.
"Here, Jack, you take the tray.
I know you will have a good time
with it."

"Oh, thank you!" said Jack.
"Come on, Susan, you can use
my sled, and I will use the tray.
This is going to be fun!"

Jack and Susan
ran out to play.

When Tommy saw
the tray, he said,
"What a funny sled!
May I have a turn
on it, Jack?"

Away went Jack
on the tray.
Around and around
he turned.

"That looks like fun,"
said Betsy to Susan.
"I want to try it."
Susan laughed.
"I do, too, now," she said.

No Fun for Susan

Susan did not want
to use the tray as a sled.

1. Did she
think of this?

2. Did she
think of this?

Fun for Jack

Here are some rhymes:

make	can	run
take	man	fun

Find the two lost rhymes.

tray

Said Susan, "No,
I will not go
Out there to play
With that big —."

box

try

Said Jack, "It's fun
To be the one
With something new
To play and —."

do

LET'S THINK AGAIN

Who Said It?

1. *Who said this?* "If Tommy gets to run the circus, I will not play."
Was he right?

2. *Who said this?* "This is my dime now."
Was he right?

3. *Who said this?* "It did help to try again!"
Was he right?

4. *Who said this?* "The boys and girls will make fun of me."
Was she right?

At School

Nancy Bobby Peter Miss White

POGO

Anne

I Can't Find It

It was time for school.

"Oh, Mother!" said Bobby.

"It's my turn to take something
for the bird at school to eat.
Do you have something he will like?"

"Yes, Bobby," said Mother.

"Here, I will put it in a box for you."

"Thank you," said Bobby.

Then he looked around.

"Did you see my hat, Mother?"

"Oh, Bobby,"
said Mother.
"Have you lost
your hat again?"

"No, I have not
lost it," said Bobby.
"I just can't find it."

"Do you have the box
for the bird?" said Mother.

"Now where did I
put it?" said Bobby
as he looked around.
"Oh, here it is!
Good-by, Mother."

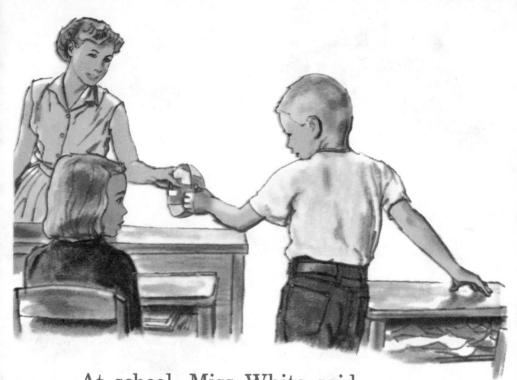

At school, Miss White said,
"Is this your hat, Bobby?
One of the boys said it was yours."

"Yes, it is," said Bobby.
"Where did he find it?"

"I do not know," said Miss White.
"But please put it away now, Bobby."
Then she said, "Boys and girls,
take out your pencils, please."

Bobby looked for his pencil.
He looked and looked.
But no pencil could Bobby find!
"Please, Anne," he said.
"Do you have a pencil I can use?"

"Have you lost your pencil again?"
said Anne.

"I have not lost it," said Bobby.
"I just can't find it."

Just then Miss White said,
"Bobby, do you have something
for the bird?
It's your turn, I think."

Bobby looked for the little box.
He looked and looked.
"I do have something here," he said.
"I know it's not lost,
but I just can't find it."

"Oh, my!" said Miss White.
"Who has something for lunch
that the bird could eat?"

"I have!" said Anne.
And she ran to get it.

When it was time to go out
and play, Bobby went to get his hat.
There was the little box,
next to his hat!
"See, Miss White!" called Bobby.
"The box was not lost, was it?"

"No, but you have lost your turn,"
said Miss White.

"I know," said Bobby.
"And this time I can't find it,
can I?"

Why Was It Lost?

1. When Bobby lost his hat,
did his mother find it?

2. When Bobby lost his pencil,
did he think he had lost it?

3. When Bobby lost the bird's lunch,
did he know where he had put it?

4. When Bobby lost his turn,
did he know why he had lost it?

Can You Find Them?

Find the lost words.

1. At home, Bobby
could not — his hat.

2. At school, Bobby
could — find his pencil.

3. Bobby said, "It is not —,
but I can't find it."

4. Miss White said, "Bobby,
— have lost your turn."

Lunch for Bobby

As Anne was going down the street,
Bobby's mother called her.
"Bobby forgot his lunch," she said.
"Will you take it to him, please?"
Then Bobby's mother said,
"Where is your lunch, Anne?
Do you take your lunch with you?"

"No, I get my lunch at school,"
said Anne.
And away she ran.

Anne's dog ran after her.
"Go home, Pogo," said Anne.
"It's no use for you to look
at Bobby's lunch like that.
This is Bobby's lunch,
and you can't have it.
Go home, now!"

But Pogo did not go home.
He went to school with Anne.

Anne looked around at school,
but she did not see Bobby.

"Come and play!" called the girls.
"Come and play, Anne!"

Anne put down the lunch.
"I will play with the girls," she said.
"Then I will take the lunch to Bobby."

This time Pogo did not run
after Anne.
He did not go with her
when she went to play.
He did not go with her
when the boys and girls
went in to school.

"Boys and girls,
who is going
to be here for lunch?"
asked Miss White.

"Oh!" said Bobby.
"I forgot my lunch!"

"Oh, Bobby!" said Anne.
"I have your lunch for you.
I put it down when I went to play."
Then Anne said, "Miss White,
may I run out and get it?"

When Anne ran out,
there was Pogo, eating Bobby's lunch.
"Stop, Pogo!" said Anne.
But it was no use.
Away ran Pogo,
and Bobby's lunch went with him!

"Oh, oh!" said Anne.
"What should I do now?"

When Anne went in, she said,
"Pogo ran away with Bobby's lunch!"
Then she said, "Here, Bobby.
You take some of my lunch money
and get your lunch at school."

"I don't like to take
your lunch money, Anne," said Bobby.
"You can't get a good lunch
with what you have there."

"I know you don't like to take
my money," said Anne.
"But I forgot your lunch, Bobby.
I think I should make up for that,
don't you?"

What Was Right?

    1. What did Anne do
with Bobby's lunch?

    2. Was that right?

    3. What did Anne do
with her lunch money?

    4. Was that right?

What Was Wrong?

    1. What did Pogo do
with Bobby's lunch?

    2. Was that wrong?

Who Knows?

    1. Did Anne know
what was right and what was wrong?

    2. Did Pogo know
what was right and what was wrong?

51

At the Bus Stop

"Come on, Peter!" called Bobby.
"It's time for the school bus."

Bobby ran down the street,
but Peter did not go with him.
"I will go when I see the bus,"
said Peter.
"When the boys and girls get on,
I will run as fast as I can.
That big boy will not have time
to run after me and take my hat."

When Peter saw the bus,
he ran as fast as he could.
But the bus had to wait for him.
The man on the bus did not like that.
"Can't you come on time?" he asked.

"Oh, my!" thought Peter.
"What will I do now?
I can't make the bus wait again.
I will have to think of something."

The next day, Peter went
to Bobby's house.

"Will you go to the bus stop
with me?" asked Peter.
"That big boy will not run after me
if you are there, too."

Bobby laughed.
"That boy could not run after you
if you did not run away," he said.
"Come on, Peter.
I will go with you."

The big boy was at the bus stop
when Bobby and Peter came.
He laughed and ran up to Peter
and Bobby.

Bobby did not run away,
but Peter did.
Away ran the big boy, after Peter!
"I am going to get you!" he called.
"I am going to take your hat!"

The next day, Peter
did not wait for Bobby.

He did not run
on the way
to the bus stop.

He did not run
when he saw
the big boy.

"This time
I am going
to surprise him,"
said Peter.

"Now I know
he will not run
after me if I
do not run away."

The big boy ran at Peter.
"I am going to get you!" he called.
But this time
Peter did not run.

The big boy
looked surprised.
"Why don't you run?"
he asked.
"It's fun
when you run away."

"It's not fun
for me," said Peter.
"Why don't you run
this time?"

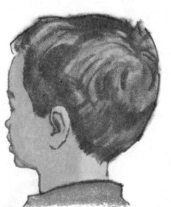

Who Ran?

1. When Peter ran away,
did the big boy run after him?

2. When Bobby did not run away,
did the big boy run after him?

3. When Peter did not run away,
did the big boy run after him?

Who Was Surprised?

1. Was Bobby surprised when
the big boy did not run after him?

2. Was the big boy surprised when
Peter did not run away?

Why Did the Big Boy Run After Peter?

1. Did he think it was fun
to make little boys run away?

2. Was it right for him
to have fun that way?

One and Two, and Then Comes Three

Nancy looked down when she saw
Miss White looking at her.

"Nancy, we are happy to have you
at May Street School," said Miss White.
"I think you will like it here."

Nancy did not look up.

"Anne, will you see that Nancy
has a good time?" asked Miss White.
"When we go out to play, will you
please take Nancy with you?"

When they went out,
Anne said to Nancy,
"Let's play hopscotch.
When we play it here,
we go:

One and two,.
And then comes three.
May Street School
Is the school for me!"

"We did not play that way
at my old school," said Nancy.
Anne looked surprised.
"Don't you want to try it?" she said.

"Oh, my!" thought Nancy.
"If I do it wrong, they will think
I don't like the way they play."
Then she said, "I don't think
I want to play hopscotch right now."

Nancy ran to the slide,
where Peter was playing.
"This slide is not as big as the one
at my old school," she said.

Peter looked surprised.
"We like it all right," he said.
"Don't you want to try it?"

"Oh yes, I am going to try it!"
said Nancy.
"I just said it is not as big."
And up the slide she went.

When Nancy came down,
Peter was not there.
She looked around, but no one
came to play with her.

Then Anne went by.
She did not stop.
She did not look at Nancy.

Nancy ran after her.
"Wait, Anne!" she said.
"Why don't you want to play with me?"

"We do want to," said Anne.
"You are the one who will not play!"

"Oh, but I will!" said Nancy.
"I want to play with all of you."

Then Anne said, "You don't like
the way we play hopscotch.
You don't like to go on the slide.
All you think about
is your old school."

"Oh, Anne!" said Nancy.
"I did not know I was doing that!
I do miss my old friends,
but I want to make new ones, too."

"Come on," said Anne.
"You can try again."

Anne and Nancy went
to play hopscotch with the girls.
"May I play?" Nancy asked them.
"I want to try it the way you play."

"This is how we do it," said Anne.

But Nancy laughed and said,
"I think I know, Anne!
  One and two,
  And then comes three.
  May Street School.
  Is the school for me!"

What Did They Think?

1. Did Anne think
that Nancy wanted to play hopscotch?

2. Did Peter think
that Nancy liked the slide?

What Did Nancy Say?

1. Did Nancy say
that she did not want to play hopscotch?

2. Did Nancy say
that she did not like the slide?

What Was Wrong?

1. Did Nancy want to make
new friends?

2. Did she know how to make
new friends?

3. Did she say too much
about her old school?

LET'S THINK AGAIN

Who Did It?

1. Who lost his turn?

2. Who ran away with Bobby's lunch?

3. Who ran away when the big boy ran after him?

4. Who learned a new way to play hopscotch?

Who Should Have Learned It?

1. Who should have learned how to make new friends?

2. Who should have learned not to run away?

3. Who should have learned to put things away?

4. Who should have learned something about her dog?

All by Myself

"Oh me, oh my!" said Peggy.
"Do you think I will have enough money
to get a big surprise for Mother?"
"Not with that!" said Will.
"But I have some money, Peggy.
I will help you get a big surprise."

"I don't want help," said Peggy.
"I want to get something all by myself."

"Come on," said Carol.
"We will go with you to help you look."

On the way, they had to stop
and get some things for Mother.
"Oh, Carol, look at this!"
called Peggy.
"I will make a cake for Mother!
How will that be for a big surprise?"

Carol laughed and said,
"Mother will like that, Peggy.
I will help you make it."

"Oh, no!" said Peggy.
"I am going to make it all by myself!"

The next day, when Mother
went out, Peggy started to work.
Carol came in to see if Peggy
could find what she wanted.

Then Will came and said,
"I know you don't want help, Peggy.
But how are you going to find out
what it says on the box?"

"I forgot about that!" said Peggy.
"But Carol can help me with that."

"What about candles?" asked Will.
"Did you get some candles, Peggy?"

"Candles!" said Peggy.
"Oh, Will, I forgot about candles!
And I have used up all my money!"

"What about the icing?" asked Will.
"A cake has to have icing."
"How do I make it?" asked Peggy.

"I will make the icing," said Carol.
"You go get the candles, Will."

"Oh, thank you!" said Peggy.
"Just help me get started,
and I will make the cake by myself."

When Peggy ran out to play,
Will and Carol went to see the cake.
"Oh, my!" laughed Carol.
"This is going to be a surprise
for Mother, all right!"

"I will call Peggy," said Will.
"She will have to clean up."

"You know she could not do it
by the time Mother comes home,"
said Carol.
"Come on, we will have to help her."

At lunch time, when Peggy came in
with the cake, Mother said, "Oh, my!
What a big surprise this is!"

"I did it all by myself,"
said Peggy. "All by myself!"

Then Will smiled at Carol,
and Carol smiled at Will.
But they did not say a word.

Who Did It?

1. Who wanted to make
a cake for Mother?

2. Who helped Peggy find things?

3. Who went to get the candles?

4. Who cleaned things up?

Who Said It?

1. Who said, "I will make the icing"?

2. Who said, "Come on,
we will have to help her"?

3. Who said, "I did it all by myself"?

4. Who did not say a word?

What Was Right?

1. Was Peggy right when she said,
"I did it all by myself"?

2. Was it right for Carol and Will
not to say a word?

In a Minute

"It's time for lunch!"
called Danny's mother.
"Come in now, Danny."

"In a minute, Mother!"
called Danny.
"I just have to make
one little street,
and then I will come."

As he started to go in,
Danny saw Will going by.
"Where are you going?"
called Danny.

"I am going to be in the parade,"
said Will.
"Oh, wait for me!" called Danny.
"I will eat lunch and go with you!"

"I can't wait," said Will.
"I have to be there on time.
You can come after lunch
with Carol and Peggy."

Danny ran into the house.

"Just look at you!" said his mother.
"Go and clean up right now."

"All right, Mother," said Danny.
"May I go to the parade after lunch?
Will is going to be in it!"

"Mother asked you to go
and clean up," said Danny's father.
"Are you going?"

Danny looked surprised.
"I am going in a minute," he said.

After lunch, Danny went out
to wait for Carol and Peggy.

"I am all ready to go," he said.
"And I think there is time
to make this little street.
I will work on it just for a minute."

"Oh, Danny, you are not ready!"
said Peggy when the girls came by.

Danny jumped up.
"I will be, in a minute," he said.

"We can't wait," said Carol.
"Come on, Peggy."

"Wait for me!" called Danny.
And he ran in to clean up again.

When Danny came out,
the girls were not there.
He ran down the street
as fast as he could.

"Where is it?" he asked a man
who was going by.
"Where is the parade?"

"Oh, you missed the parade!"
said the man.
"You missed it just by a minute."

What Did He Do?

Did Danny do what he should
when he was asked
to do something?

What Did He Say?

What did Danny say
when he was asked to do something?

What Would They Say?

1. If you called
this man for help,
would he say,
"In a minute"?

2. Would this man say,
"In a minute"?

3. Would this man say,
"In a minute"?

A Good, Big Fire

"Peggy! Peggy!" called Will
when he saw her jump in the leaves.
"Oh, Peggy, don't do that!"

"This is fun!" laughed Peggy.
"I like to play in the leaves."

"Oh, Peggy!" said Will.
"Now I will have to clean up
all the leaves again."

Peggy laughed.
"If I help you, will you let me
jump on them?" she asked.
"No," said Will.
"The leaves are not to play in."

Then Will said, "I know something
you would like, Peggy.
If you help me clean up the leaves
again, we could have a fire."

"Did Mother say
we could start a fire?" asked Peggy.

"Not when she is away," said Will.
"But I think we could start one
when she comes home."

"Then I will help you," said Peggy.
"I like a good, big fire."

By and by, Peggy ran
into the house.
When she came out again,
she had a box of matches.
"We have enough leaves now to make
a good, big fire," she said to Will.
"You said we could have one."

"No, Peggy!" called Will.
"We can't have one now.
We will ask Mother to start one
when she comes home."

Peggy laughed at Will.
"You are afraid," she said.
"You are afraid of a fire!"

"Give me the matches!" said Will,
as he started to run.
But it was no use.
By then, Peggy had put a match
to the leaves, and the fire jumped up.

Now Peggy was afraid.
"Help!" she called. "Will, help me!"

Will ran and pulled Peggy
out of the way of the fire.
"Peggy, are you all right?" he said.

"Yes," said Peggy.
"But it's a good thing I was wrong
when I said you were afraid!"

"You were not wrong!" said Will.
"Peggy, there are some things
it is good to be afraid of.
And a good, big fire is one of them!"

What Was Will Doing?

1. Was he playing?
2. Was he working?
3. Was he doing what he should do?

What Was Peggy Doing?

1. Was she playing?
2. Was she working?
3. Was she doing what she should do?

Who Was Helping?

1. Was Will trying to help Mother?
2. Was Peggy trying to help Mother?
3. Was Peggy trying to help Will?
4. Was Will trying to help Peggy?

Who Was Afraid?

1. Was Peggy afraid to play with matches?
2. Was Will afraid to play with matches?
3. Who was right?

Jack's New Train

Jack looked at the train
in the big box.
For a minute, he was so happy
he did not know what to say.

Then he said, "Oh, thank you,
Uncle Peter, thank you!"

"Look what was in my box!"
cried little Betsy Anne.
"A toy duck!
It can say *quack-quack*."

Jack started the new train.
Clickety-clack, it went.
Clickety-clack, clickety-clack.

Betsy Anne put down her duck.
"I want to try it," she said.
"I want to run the new train."

"No, you don't know how
to run a train," said Jack.
"Can't you play with your duck?"

"I don't want to play
with my duck," said Betsy Anne.
"I want to run the new train."

Clickety-clack, clickety-clack.
The train came to a stop.
"O.K., you can try it," said Jack.

Betsy Anne started the train
too fast.
Clickety-clack, clickety —
Down went the train!
"Now look what you did!" cried Jack.

"Oh, Jack!" said Uncle Peter.
"The train is all right.
Betsy Anne just started it too fast.
Look, I will start it again."

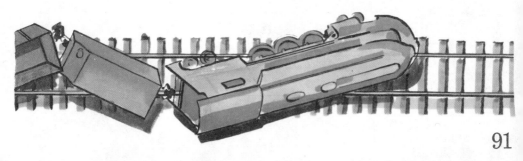

When the train started again,
Betsy Anne did not look at it.
She did not look at Jack.
She did not play with her new duck.

Clickety-clack, clickety-clack,
went the train.
But now it did not make Jack happy.

"What can I do?" he thought.
"I can see why she wants
to play with my train.
But she is too little to run it right."

Then Uncle Peter said,
"Jack, why don't you let the duck
ride on the train?"

"Oh!" cried Betsy Anne.
"My duck would like that!"

All at once Jack was happy again.
He put the duck on the train.
"Here we go!" said Jack.
Quack-quack, said the duck.
*Clickety-clack, clickety-clack,
clickety-clack,* said Jack's new train.

What Makes This Sound?

1. What makes a sound like *clickety-clack?*

2. What makes a sound like *quack?*

3. Could a duck make a sound like *clickety-clack?*

4. Could a boy make a sound like *clickety-clack?*

What Makes a Toy Good?

1. Was a train a good toy for Jack?

2. Was a duck a good toy for Betsy Anne?

3. Would a duck be a good toy for Jack?

4. Would a train be a good toy for Betsy Anne?

5. Would a duck be a good toy for a boy as little as Betsy Anne?

6. Would a train be a good toy for a girl as big as Jack?

Golden Keys of Courtesy

A bunch of golden keys is mine
To make each day with gladness shine.
"Good morning," that's the golden key
That opens every day to me.
When evening comes, "Good-night," I say,
And close the door of each glad day.
When at the table, "If you please"
I take from off my bunch of keys.
When friends do anything for me,
I use the little "Thank you" key.
If by mistake some harm I do,
"Excuse me," "I beg your pardon," too—
Or if unkindly hurt I've given,
"I'm sorry, forgive me"—I'll be forgiven.
On a golden chain these keys I'll bind,
They'll help me always to be kind.

Author Unknown

LET'S THINK AGAIN

In What Story Did You Find It?

1. What story was about
a boy, a girl, and some leaves?

2. What story was about
a boy and a parade?

3. What story was about
two girls, a boy, and a cake?

4. What story was about
a duck that had a ride?

Was It Wrong?

1. Was it wrong for Danny to say,
"Wait a minute"?

2. Was it wrong for Will to say,
"Wait for Mother to make a fire"?

3. Was it wrong for Peggy to say,
"I did it all by myself"?

4. Was it wrong for Jack
to run his train by himself?

At Work

Something to Wait For

"That looks as if it's going to be
a good airplane," said Jimmy.
"Some day, Bill, will you make me
one like that?"

"Some day I may surprise you,"
said Bill.
"But right now you can help me
by finding a pencil.
I have to go and get something,
but I will be back in a minute."

When Bill went out, Jimmy started
to look for a pencil.

That was when he saw the money.

"Oh, Bill has three dimes here!"
he said to himself.

"I think I will ask him if I
may have a dime for some candy."

Jimmy helped himself
to one of the dimes.

"I know Bill would let me
have this if I asked him," he thought.

"I will get the candy now and
tell him about it when I come back."

As Jimmy came out of the house,
he said to himself, "Bill likes candy.
I will get some for him, too.
Then everything will be all right."

Jimmy started to run.
"Yes," he said to himself.
"Bill likes candy as much as I do!
Everything will be all right."

But when Jimmy came back,
everything was not all right.
He thought, "Bill may not like it
when he finds out about the dime.
What will he say
when he sees the candy?"

Then Jimmy put the candy away
where Bill would not see it.

Jimmy went to look for Bill.

"Is your airplane just about ready?"
he asked.

"No, I could not find
what I was looking for," said Bill.
"Then I thought I would go out
and get the things I wanted.
But some of my money is missing.
I know I had one more dime.
Do you see it around here, Jimmy?"

Jimmy looked around for a minute.
"No, Bill, I don't see it," he said.

"I am sorry, Jimmy," said Bill.
"But now you will have to wait
for your airplane.
When I get some more money,
I will work on it again."

"My airplane!" cried Jimmy.
"I thought this airplane was for you."
"No, it's for you," said Bill.
"I was going to surprise you."
Then Bill laughed and said, "You
don't look too happy about it, Jimmy.
Don't you like my surprise?"

"Oh, yes! I just don't like to have
to wait for my airplane," said Jimmy.
But he did not sound happy
when he said it.
And he did not look happy
as he ran out.

When Jimmy came back, he said,
"Bill, I have a surprise for you, too.
But it's not going to make you happy."

Bill saw the candy that Jimmy had.
"Candy will make me happy!" he said.
"Not this candy!" said Jimmy.
"I used your dime to get it!"

"Oh!" said Bill. "I see."
"I am sorry, Bill!" said Jimmy.
"Will you ever let me help you again?"

"Some day I may surprise you,"
said Bill.
"But now you will have to wait
for that, too!"

What Did Jimmy Think?

1. Did Jimmy think it was right
to take the dime?

2. Did he try to make himself
think it was right?

3. Did he really make himself
think it was right?

What Did Jimmy Do?

1. Did Jimmy put the dime back?

2. Did he tell Bill about the dime?

3. Did he say he was sorry?

Is It All Right?

1. Is it all right
to do something wrong
if you say you are sorry?

2. Is it all right
not to say you are sorry
if you do something wrong?

One Little Indian

Tommy and Dick were waiting
to play Indian when Paul came out.
"How!" said Paul.
"Me big Indian!"

"How!" said Dick.
"You funny Indian.
What you want that
funny thing for?"

"We make tent,"
said Paul.
"Make big tent.
Then have big fun
playing Indian!"

Then Paul looked around and said,
"We will have to have some sticks."
"I have one at home," said Tommy.

"One is not enough," said Paul.
"It takes three sticks for a tent."
Then Paul went away for a minute.
He came back with a big, big stick.
"We can saw this in two," he said.
"With your stick, Tommy,
that will be enough for the tent."
"This is starting to sound
like work!" said Tommy.
"When are we going to play Indian?"

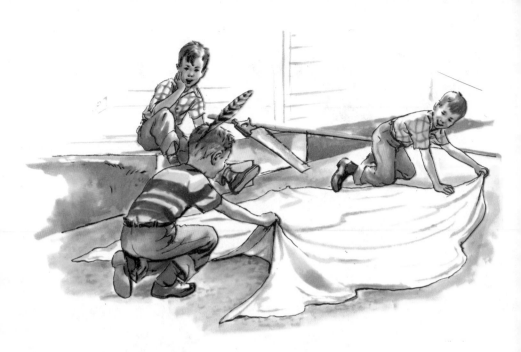

Dick and Paul just laughed at Tommy.
Then Dick said, "If we had some paint,
we could paint things on the tent."
"I have some paint!" said Paul.
"I will run and get it."

"What do you want to do
all that work for?" asked Tommy.
"A white tent will be just as good!"
"It will not be much work
if everyone helps," said Paul.

Three little Indians started to work.

Just then, Bill came by.

"Who wants to play ball?" he called.

"I do!" called Tommy, and away he ran.

Two little Indians went on working.

Then Dick's white kitten ran up.

"Don't let her get in the paint!" cried Paul.

But by the time Dick turned around,

the kitten was red, white, and yellow.

"Oh, my!" laughed Dick.

And he went home to clean her up.

One little Indian went on working.
He put some more paint
where the kitten had jumped.

He painted a big red pony
and two yellow birds.

Then he went to work on the stick.

After he sawed it in two,
he went to get Tommy's stick.

Then he was ready to put up the tent.

When Tommy came to play Indian,
he said, "How! Me be Indian chief."
    Then Dick ran up and said,
"How! Me be Indian chief."

    Paul looked at them and laughed.
"How!" he said.
"Me make whole tent myself.
Me do all work myself.
Me think ME be Indian chief
this time!"

Who Wanted to Play?

1. Did Tommy want to play Indian?
2. Did Dick?
3. Did Paul?

Who Thought of What to Do?

1. Who thought of the tent?
2. Who thought of the sticks?
3. Who thought of sawing
the big stick in two?

Who Did the Work?

1. Who sawed the stick in two?
2. Who painted the tent?
3. Who put up the tent?

Who Should Be Chief?

1. Did Tommy want to be chief?
2. Did Dick want to be chief?
3. Did Paul want to be chief?
4. Which boy should be chief?

Enough for Everyone

Julie was helping her father.
"Oh, here is where the carrots are!"
she said.
"I hope you put in enough of them.
I like carrots!"

Father laughed.
"We all like carrots," he said.
"I think there will be
enough for everyone, Julie."

Day after day, Julie went out
to see how big the carrots were.
When Tommy came to play with her,
she would take him to see them, too.

One day Tommy said, "I think
they are big enough to eat now, Julie."

Julie pulled up a carrot.
"Oh, how little it is!" she cried.
"Try some more," said Tommy.
"They can't all be as little as that!"
But all the carrots Julie pulled up
were much too little to eat.

Julie looked at the little carrots.

"Oh, Tommy!" she said.

"Father will not like it
when he sees that I pulled them up."

"Why don't you give them
to the rabbit?" said Tommy.

"Then if your father says,
'Did you eat them?' you can say no.
It will be the truth, too."

Julie did not know what to do.
But she had to do something,
so she let the rabbit eat the carrots.

When Father came home, he said,
"Someone started eating the carrots.
Was it you, Julie?"

"No, Father," said Julie.
"It was the rabbit!"

"Did you let him out?" asked Father.
"Oh, I would not do that!" said Julie.

Then Father said, "I don't think
the rabbit could get out by himself.
But we can tell in a minute if he did.
Come on, Julie. Let's go and see."

When they went out,
Father looked around for a minute.
Then he said, "You see, Julie,
the rabbit did not get out.
Even if he did eat the carrots,
someone had to give them to him."

"Who do you think did it?"
asked Julie.

"I don't know," said Father.
"Do you know, Julie?"

Julie could not look at her father.
"Yes, I know," she said. "I did it."

At first, Father did not say a word.
Then he said, "By and by, Julie,
the first carrots will be ready.
But I am afraid there will not be
enough for you."

"But you said we would have
enough for everyone!" cried Julie.

"We did have!" said Father.
"But you let the rabbit eat yours.
Now I hope there will be enough
for everyone else.
We all like carrots, you know."

Is It the Truth?

Would Julie be telling the truth
if she said this?

1. "I did not eat the carrots."

2. "I did not let the rabbit out."

3. "At first, I did not know
that the carrots were too little to eat."

4. "I did not pull up the carrots."

5. "Tommy said he would make me
give the carrots to the rabbit."

Is It the Whole Truth?

Did Julie tell her father
everything he wanted to know
when he asked this?

1. "Did you eat the carrots?"

2. "Did you let the rabbit out?"

3. "Do you know who did give
the carrots to the rabbit?"

Is It Right?

Is it right to tell
just some of the truth
when you know the whole truth?

I cleaned my room and made my bed
And did just what my mother said.
That's why I have this happy grin
And wear a Mother's Helper pin.

I raked the yard, as Father would,
And shined my shoes the way I should.
I did the best that I could do.
That's why I wear a new pin, too.

Who Gets It?

This is a story that has no ending.
How do you think it should end?

"Did someone really give away
this little blue train?" asked Davy.
"It looks like a new one to me!"
"Yes," said Miss Best.
"It's a good train, and someone
in the hospital will be happy to get it."

Davy laughed.
"I know I would!" he said.

Not all the toys
that came in
were as good as
the little train.

But it was fun
to work on
the old ones.

It was fun
to clean them
and paint them
and make them
look new again.

121

It was fun to go around
and get the toys, too.

After school, Davy started out
to get some more.

People were happy to give old toys
for the boys and girls in the hospital.
In no time at all,
Davy had a pony, a doll, and a boat.

At the next house,
a man let him have a jack-in-the-box.
Now he had all he could take
at once, so he started home.

On his way, Davy saw Mr. Wills.
"Look, Mr. Wills!" called Davy.
"We are going to take old toys
to the children in the hospital."

"Oh, I would like to give some toys
for them, too," said Mr. Wills.
"Come around to my house
after you take home what you have."

"But there are no children
at your house, Mr. Wills!" said Davy.
"There used to be!" said Mr. Wills.
"You come around to my house, Davy.
I will see what I can find for you."

When Davy came back,
Mr. Wills did not look happy at all.
"I looked and looked," he said.
"But I could not find the old toys
that we used to have around here.
This pogo stick was all there was.
You may have it
if you think it will help."

"Oh boy, a pogo stick!" said Davy.
"Thank you, Mr. Wills, thank you!"

Down the street went Davy
on the pogo stick.
Up and down! Up and down!
What fun it was!

Then he started
to think.

"Why should I
give this pogo stick
to the children
in the hospital?
They can't use it,
but I can.

"Why can't I
keep it for myself?"

*Is it all right for Davy to keep
the pogo stick?*
*What would you tell him if he asked
you about it?*

What If You Were in a Hospital?

1. If the hospital would let
your friends see you,
would you want them to come?

2. Would you like to have your friends
give you things to play with?

What If a Friend Were in a Hospital?

1. Would you go to see your friend
if you could?

2. Would you take something
for your friend to play with?

What About Children You Do Not Know?

1. Would they like
to have other children
come to see them?

2. Would they like
to have things
to play with?

3. What can you do
about that?

Because I'm Happy

Thank You, God, for legs to run
With my pup out in the sun.
Thank You for my eyes to see
Bright new leaves on every tree.
Then, dear God, I'd like to say
Thank You for this summer day.

LET'S THINK AGAIN

Who Did Not Wait?

    1. Who did not wait
to ask for some money?

    2. Who did not wait
for someone to help him make a tent?

    3. Who did not wait
for something to be big enough to eat?

Who Was Sorry?

    1. Was Jimmy sorry
that he did not wait
to ask Bill for the dime?

    2. Was Julie sorry
that she did not wait
for the carrots to be big enough?

    3. Was Paul sorry
that he did not wait
for Dick and Tommy to help him?

At Party Time

129

WHAT GEORGE FORGOT

"Good-by, Mother," said George.
"I am ready to go to the party."
"Oh, George, you funny boy!"
laughed Mother.
"You are not going to Bobby's party
like that, are you?"

"Yes," said George.
"I am going to take this hat.
It will help me at the party."
Then he ran to get something else.

"I think I will take this, too,"
said George when he came back.

"What for?"
asked his mother.
"Don't you think
they will have
things to play with
at the party?"

"Oh yes, I guess so," said George.
"But this will help me have fun.
I know something else
that will help me, too."
And he ran to get it.

"Is this a game?" asked Mother
when George came in again.
"You are not going to take THAT
to a birthday party, are you?"

"Yes, I am," said George.
"It will help me make friends."
"How?" asked Mother.

"Boys and girls like to play
with things like this," said George.
"When they play with my toys,
they will play with me, too."
And he ran to get something else.

"Look, George," said his mother
when George came back this time.
"You have to take this box of things
that Bobby's mother asked for.
I don't see how you are going to take
all your toys with you, too."

"Could you take the box
for Bobby's mother?" asked George.
"It would take you just a minute."
"Why, yes, I guess so," said Mother.
"All right, I will take the box.
But we will have to go right now."

At first George thought everything
would be all right at the party.
Everyone liked his toys
and wanted to play with them.

But then he saw
that something was wrong.

The children did play with his toys,
but they did not play with him!

"Oh, my!" he said to himself.
"What will I do now?"

When George's mother was ready
to go, she said, "I think
you forgot something, George.
There is one more thing that
you really should have at a party."

"I can see that something
is wrong," said George.
"What is it that I forgot?"

"Your smile!" said his mother.
"How can you make friends at a party
when you do not have a smile?"

"Oh, Mother!" laughed George.
"That is it! That is what I forgot!"

What Did George Want?

1. Did George want to go
to the party?

2. Did he want to have a good time
at the party?

3. Did he want to help other children
have a good time, too?

What Did George Do?

1. Did George take some things
to the party?

2. Did he let the other children
play with his toys?

3. Did he do everything
he could think of to help the party?

4. Was there one thing
that George did not think of?

The Red Shoes

Laura looked at Patsy's new dress.
"Oh, Patsy, it's just right
for your birthday party!" she said.
"Do you have red shoes to go with it?"

"Red shoes would be just right,"
said Patsy.
"But I have no red shoes.
My old white ones will have to do."

When Laura went home, she said,
"Mother, could I give Patsy
shoes for her birthday?"

"Shoes for her doll?" asked Mother.
"I thought you were going
to give the doll a big blue hat."

"No, I am talking about
shoes for Patsy," said Laura.
"Patsy has no red shoes
to go with her new red dress.
I can tell it's what she really wants.
And it's fun to get what you
really want for your birthday."

"Yes, it is fun to get what you
really want," said Laura's mother.
"But you can't get shoes for Patsy
all by yourself, Laura.
It would take too much money."

Mother thought for a minute.
"Do you think the other children
would give some money?" she asked.
"You could get enough for red shoes
that way."

"Oh, yes!" cried Laura.
"That would be fun!
I will go ask everyone right now."

First Laura went to ask Susan
about giving red shoes to Patsy.

Susan thought it sounded like fun,
and she went with Laura to Peggy's.

Peggy thought it would be fun, too,
so she went with Laura to Bill's.

Bill thought it would be fun, too.
So Bill and Peggy and Susan
went with Laura to Bobby's.

Then Bobby said yes, it sounded
like fun, and he went with Laura
to Carol's.

And Carol said yes,
and Danny said yes,
and Fred said yes.

Everyone said yes,
it would be fun for Patsy
to get what she really wanted.

The next day, the boys and girls
went to see Patsy.

"We have a surprise for you,"
said Laura.
"We are giving it to you now,
so you will have it for your party."

When Patsy saw what was in the box,
she was too happy for words.
Then she looked around at everyone
and said. "Thank you, oh thank you!
I don't know how you guessed it,
but red shoes are just what I wanted!"

Who Thought of It?

1. Who thought of red shoes
to go with Patsy's new red dress?

2. Who thought of giving red shoes
for Patsy's birthday?

Who Did It?

1. Who asked everyone to help?
2. Who helped?

Who Was Happy?

1. Did the red shoes
make Patsy happy?

2. Did giving Patsy the red shoes
make everyone happy?

3. Did asking everyone to help
make Laura happy?

What Makes People Happy?

1. Does it make people happy
to get something they want?

2. Does it make people happy
to give something to someone?

Next Time

"I hope I win a prize at your party,
Candy," said Nancy May.
"Is there a prize for this game?"
"Yes, there are prizes
for all the games," said Candy.
"And there will even be a prize
at the end for the best loser!"

Then the game started.
Around and around went the children,
laughing and talking as they went.

When it was time to stop,
Nancy May was the first one out.
"That was not fair!" she cried.
"Everyone was talking so much,
I could not tell
that it was time to stop.
Let's start the game again."

"Oh, no!" said Candy.
"You are out, Nancy May.
Maybe you will win the next time."

The next game was "touch."
When everyone was ready, Candy
came in with a tray of little things.

"Nancy May, you may be first
to touch and guess," said Candy.
"The one who knows everything
at the end, wins."

It was fun to touch the things
and try to guess what they were.

"I can tell what all of them are!"
cried Nancy May.
"This time I am going to win!"

After everyone else
had a turn at guessing,
Candy put away
the tray.

Then the children
had to tell
Candy's mother
what they thought
they had touched.

"Peggy wins!" said Candy's mother
after everyone had a turn.

"That is not fair!" said Nancy May.
"I had to wait for all the others.
How could I think of everything
after all that time?"

"Peggy wins, Nancy May,"
said Candy's mother.
"Maybe you will win
the next time."

"Here I go!" said Nancy May
when her turn came in the next game.
"I hope I win this time!"

The children laughed when Nancy May
started to go the wrong way.
The more they laughed,
the more she went the wrong way.

"That was not fair!" said Nancy May
when she saw where she was.
"I think you started me wrong!
How could I get all the way down here?"

Just then Candy's mother
called them to come and eat.
"First I have to give the prize
for the best loser," said Candy.

"Oh!" thought Nancy May.
"Maybe I will get a prize after all!
No one lost as much as I did!"
But Candy was not looking at her.
"I am looking for a happy loser,"
said Candy.

"A happy loser?" said Nancy May.
"Is that what you call a good loser?"
Then Nancy May laughed.
"Yes, I guess it is!" she said.
"And I guess I will have to learn
how to be one.
Then maybe I will win a prize
the next time!"

Did She Win Something?

1. Did Nancy May
win all three games?

2. Did she win two games?

3. Did she win one game?

4. Did she win the prize
for being the best loser?

Could She Learn Something?

1. Could Nancy May learn
how to win some games?

2. Could she learn
how to be a good loser?

Could Everyone Learn Something?

1. Could everyone learn
how to win all games?

2. Could everyone learn
how to win some games?

3. Could everyone learn
how to be a good loser?

THE PONY PARTY

"I am so sorry for Peter!" said Laura.
"Now that he has hurt himself,
he can't have his birthday party."

"I am sorry he hurt himself, too,"
said Danny.
"He wanted that party so much!
A man was going to come with a pony
and take us all for rides.

"Peter was so happy when his mother
thought of giving him that party!
Now he will not have a pony party
after all."

All at once Laura started to laugh.

Danny looked surprised.

"What is so funny about missing
a party with pony rides?" he asked.

"I was not thinking
about the party," said Laura.
"I was thinking about a pony that
Father and I saw at the circus.

"It was not really a pony.
It was two people dressed up
like a pony.
They were ever so funny!"

"What did they do?" asked Danny.

"Oh, they galloped around
and ran into things," said Laura.
"They were so funny
we could not stop laughing,
even after they went away."

"Say!" cried Danny.
"I know what we can do!
Let's dress up like the circus people
and have a pony party for Peter!"

"Yes, a surprise party!" cried Laura.
"We can even have two ponies.
Patsy and I can be one,
and you and Fred can be the other.
We can gallop around like this."

Danny laughed.
"Let's get to work," he said.
"You go call Patsy and Fred.
I will run and ask my mother
for something to make the ponies with."

The children worked and worked
on the ponies, but it was fun.
They laughed as much as they worked.

Patsy and Laura
were ready first.
"Come on!"
said Patsy,
and she started
to gallop.
But Laura
did not know
that Patsy
was starting.

Away went Patsy,
but the other end of the pony
did not go with her!
Then Patsy could not keep up
the whole pony, and down she went!

The two boys
laughed and laughed.
"All right," said Laura.
"Let's see you try it."

"O.K.," said Danny.
"Here we go!"
And he started
to gallop away.

But Fred was not ready, so Danny
ran into him, and down went that pony!

"See, Danny?" laughed Laura.
"You can't be a pony all by yourself!
We will really have to work at it,
if we want to do this right."

On Peter's birthday,
the children went to his house
dressed up like ponies.

Peter laughed and laughed
when they came galloping in.
"Oh!" he cried.
"I thought I was not going
to have fun at all on my birthday.
But now it's turning out to be
the best birthday I ever had!"

Let's Suppose

1. Suppose Peter could have had his pony party.

A. Would Peter have had a good time?

B. Would his friends have had a good time?

2. Suppose no one had thought of giving a surprise party for Peter.

A. Would Peter have had a good time?

B. Would his friends have had a good time?

3. Suppose no one had wanted to work.

A. Did the children have to work to make the ponies?

B. Did they have to work to learn how to gallop?

C. If they had not worked, would they have had fun?

LET'S THINK AGAIN

Which Is the Right Word?

1. Patsy wanted red shoes
for her (birthday, doll).

2. George forgot
his (lunch, smile).

3. Peter's friends
were dressed as (Indians, ponies).

4. Nancy May wanted
to win a (prize, pony).

Which Is the Wrong Rhyme?

Two of the words that rhyme are wrong.
What should they be?

"We want some fun!"
The children cried.
"Why can't we have
A pony slide?"

"It is not fair,"
Said Nancy May.
"I do not win
The games I say."

At Story Time

Hoja

Daniel's
King

Daniel

The Boy
Who Cried
Wolf

The King
Who Could Not
Smile

Daniel

There once was a man called Daniel,
and he was a good man.
The King liked him and trusted him
as he trusted no one else.

But there were some people
who did not like Daniel.

"Let us find some wrong in him,"
they said.
"The King would like us more
if he did not like Daniel so much."

But Daniel was
a good man,
and the people
could find
no wrong.

Then one man said,
"Daniel prays
three times a day.
When he prays, he gives thanks
to his God, not to the King.
"If the King says
no man may do this,
Daniel will be in the wrong."

Then the people went to the King.
"O King!" they said.
"It is not right that some
of your people do not pray to you.
You should order everyone to do so.
And he who will not pray to you
should be put in with the lions."

The King did not know that Daniel
prayed three times a day to his God.
So he said, "So be it!
He who does not pray to me
will be put in with the lions."

Daniel was not afraid.
He would not stop praying to God.

So the people went again
to the King and said, "O King!
Daniel prays to his God,
and not to you.
By your order, he should be
put in the den with the lions."

How sorry the King was then!
He wanted to help Daniel,
but he could not take back his order.

So Daniel was put in the lions' den.
"May the God that you trust
be of help to you now," said the King.

When the King went away,
he thought of no one but Daniel.
He would not eat.
He would not talk to the people
who came to see him.

His thoughts were on Daniel
in the lions' den.

The next day
the King went
to the lions' den.
"Daniel! Daniel!"
he cried.
"How is it with you?"

"God has not let the lions hurt me,"
said Daniel.
And he came out of the den,
and the King saw that it was so.

Then the King was happy,
and he put out this order:
"The God who helped Daniel
is a good God.
He will be the God of my people
for ever and ever more."

Could Daniel Be Trusted?

1. Was Daniel a man
who could be trusted?

2. Did the King know
that Daniel could be trusted?

3. Did the people think
that Daniel could not be trusted?

4. Did they try to make it look
as if Daniel could not be trusted?

Which Was Wrong?

1. Was it wrong for Daniel
to pray to his God?

2. Was it wrong for Daniel
not to pray to the King?

3. Was it wrong to make the King
think that Daniel could not be trusted?

Who Helped Daniel?

1. Once Daniel was in the lions' den,
could the King help him?

2. Could the people help him?

3. Could God help him?

4. Did God help him?

THE BOY WHO CRIED WOLF

A boy once went to work
for a man who had some sheep.
"There will not be much
for you to do," said the man.
"But do look out for the wolf!"

"Do you think the wolf will come?"
asked the boy.

"Who knows?" said the man.
"But if you see him, call out.
I will come and help you."

On the first day,
everything was all right.
There was not much to do,
and the boy liked his new work.

But the next day he started wanting
someone to talk to.

Then the boy
had a thought.

"If the man thinks
the wolf has come,
he will run
to help me.

"That will be fun,
and I will have
someone to talk to."

So he cried out,
"The wolf! The wolf!
The wolf has come!"

The man came on the run.
All the people working with him
came, too.

Then they saw
that the wolf was not there.
"The boy was playing a joke,"
said the man.
So everyone laughed and went away.

The next day,
the boy thought it would be fun
to play the joke again.

So he cried, "The wolf! The wolf!
The wolf has come!"
And again, all the people
ran to help him.

But this time they did not laugh
when they saw it was a joke.
No one thought it was funny, now,
at all.

"Let this be the end of your jokes,"
said the man.
"We have work to do, and so do you."

Then the day came
when the wolf really did come.
The boy was afraid.
"Help! Help!" he cried.
"The wolf is here.
Come and help me!"
Again and again he cried out,
but no help came.
"I will have to leave the sheep
and go for help myself," he said.
And away he ran, calling all the time.

When the boy saw the man, he cried,
"Help! Help! Come at once!
The wolf is eating the sheep!"

At first everyone thought
he was playing a joke again.
But when they saw it was not a joke,
they ran to help the sheep.

One man was too old to run.
He came up to the boy and said,
"This time the joke is on you.
No one trusts you now,
even when you tell the truth!"

Did the Boy Tell the Truth?

Three times the boy called,
"The wolf has come!"

1. Did he tell the truth
the first time?

2. Did he tell the truth
the next time?

3. Did he ever tell the truth?

Did the Man Trust the Boy?

1. Did the man trust the boy
the first time?

2. Did he trust the boy
the next time?

3. Did he trust the boy
after the first two times?

What Do You Think?

1. Could a boy like this one
learn to tell the truth?

2. Could a man like this one
learn to trust the boy?

The King Who Could Not Smile

There once was a King who did
all he could to make his people happy.
But there was one thing
that the King could not do.
He did not know how to smile!
Now this King was a good King,
and his people did everything he did.

If the King had carrot cake for lunch,
the people had carrot cake, too.
If the King put on a red hat,
the people put on red hats, too.

But if the King did not smile,
the people did not smile.
So no one was happy after all.

The King was sorry about this,
for he wanted his people to be happy.
So he said, "I will give a big prize
if someone can make me smile."

One by one,

people came to try to win the prize.

And one by one,
they went away,
for no one
could make
the King smile.

Then one day the King went
for a ride on a bus.
He dressed in old things
so no one would know who he was.

"What do you think
we should do about the King?"
he asked a little boy.

"I think it would be best
if we forgot about him," said the boy.

"Oh, no!" said the King.
"Not that!"

"Oh, yes!" said the little boy.
"We should stop doing what he does
and do what we want to do.
This way, no one has fun at all."

All the way home, the King thought
about what the little boy had said.
The next day, he put out this order:

The King orders his people
to stop doing everything he does.
Eat what you please, do what
you please, and SMILE *if you please.*
                    By Order of the King.

At first people could not get used
to doing what they wanted.
But in time they did.

If the King had cake
with white icing, some people
had cake with blue icing.

If the King put on a red hat,
some people put on yellow hats.

People were so happy about this
that they just had to smile.
And when the King saw the smiles
of his people, he had to smile, too.

One day the King went again
for a ride on the bus.
Up and down the streets he went,
looking at the happy people.

He smiled at the people,
and the people smiled at him.
And this time the King could not
make them stop doing what he did.
For if there is one thing you can't
keep to yourself, it's a smile.

Try it, and you will see!

Were They Happy?

1. Was the King who could not smile
a happy man?

2. Were his people happy?

3. Did the King
want to be happy?

4. Did he want his people
to be happy, too?

Could You Be Happy?

1. Are you happy
when you want to smile?

2. Are you happy
when you don't want to smile?

3. Could you be happy
if you could not smile?

Can Someone Else Make You Happy?

When someone smiles at you,
do you want to smile, too?

THE OTHER WAY AROUND

In days of old, there was
a man called Hoja
who had a big garden.
    One fair day he went out
to his garden to work.

"God is good to me," said Hoja,
as he looked around.
"Just see how everything grows!
I have much to give thanks for,
with a garden as fair as this."

There was much to do
in the garden,
and Hoja was happy
as he worked.

After a time
he wanted
something to eat.
"I think I would like
some watermelon,"
said he.
And he went
to the watermelon vines
to get one.

Hoja looked at all the vines
for a watermelon that was ready to eat.

Then he saw one that he liked,
just big enough, but not too big.

As he started to take it,
he smiled.

"Just think!" he said to himself.
"This watermelon is three times
as big as my hat.

"But it does not grow on a tree,
as one would suppose.
It grows on a little vine,
not even as big as a stick!
Now that is something to think about!"

In the garden there was a nut tree
where Hoja liked to eat his lunch.
He went there with the watermelon.

As he was eating, he looked up
at the tree.

"I suppose God knows
what is best," he thought.
"But how can this be right?

"He makes little nuts
grow on big trees and big watermelons
grow on little vines.

"I would have had it
the other way around, if I were God!"

Just then a nut
came down,
right on Hoja.

Hoja was surprised,
but the nut
did not hurt him.

All at once, he started to laugh.

"In truth, O God!" he said.
"Now I see how little I know!
What if a watermelon,
and not a nut,
had come down on me?
That would not be
so funny!

"You who know
everything
have put things
where they should be —
nuts, watermelons,
and all!"

If Things Were the Other Way Around

Tell what is wrong.

1.

2.

3.

4.

5.

6.

LET'S THINK AGAIN

Who Was It?

    1. Did the King who could not smile put Daniel in the lions' den?

    2. Did the boy who cried wolf find a watermelon?

    3. Did Hoja try to make the King smile?

Who Learned It?

    1. Who learned that it is best to tell the truth?

    2. Who learned that the best way to make people smile is to smile yourself?

    3. Who learned that God's way is the best way?

    4. Who learned that God will help us if we pray?

VOCABULARY INFORMATION

This first reader contains 158 new words, exclusive of proper names, which are introduced on unit title pages and are also included in the picture dictionary of proper names on pages 190–192.

A word is counted as new if it (or a variant formed by the addition of *s*, *es*, *'s*, *s'*, *d*, *ed*, or *ing*) is not in the American Book Company Core Vocabulary for Use in First Readers. This Core Vocabulary is composed of words common to at least five out of eight series of basic pre-primers and primers. Poems are excluded from the vocabulary control.

Maximum new words per sentence	1
Maximum new words per page	2
Maximum new words per story	8
Maximum new words per activity	2
Maximum words per sentence	15

UNIT 1

7. *Susan*
   Tommy
   Betsy
8. circus
9. ....
10. hat
11. if
12. think
    that
13. when
14. be
15. ....
16. win
17. time
    try
18. again
    can't
19. know
20. as
21. why
22. dime
    street
23. candy
24. lost
25. work

26. around
    how
27. some
28. ....
29. sled
    snow
30. use
31. tray
32. could
    her
33. ....
34. turn
35. rhymes
    it's
36. let's
    right

UNIT 2

37. school
    Bobby
    Anne
    Pogo
    Miss White
    Peter
    Nancy
38. bird
39. just

40. pencils
41. his
42. lunch
43. next
    called
44. words
    them
45. forgot
    him
46. after
47. ....
48. asked
49. should
50. money
    don't
51. wrong
52. bus
53. wait
    thought
54. day
55. ....
56. way
57. ....
58. ....
59. ....
60. hopscotch
    old

61. slide
62. by
63. about
    friends
64. ....
65. say
    much
66. learned
    things

UNIT 3

67. *Carol*
    Peggy
    Danny
    Uncle Peter
68. myself
    enough
69. cake
70. started
    candles
71. icing
72. clean
73. smiled
74. ....
75. minute
76. parade
77. ....

78. ready
79. . . . .
80. were
81. would
82. fire
    leaves
83. let
84. . . . .
85. matches
86. afraid
    give
87. pulled
88. . . . .
89. so
    cried
90. clickety-
    clack
91. . . . .
92. . . . .
93. once
94. sound
96. story
    himself

UNIT 4

97. *Bill*
    Jimmy
    Dick
    Paul
    Julie
    Davy
    Miss Best
    Mr. Wills
98. back
99. tell
100. everything
101. more

102. sorry
103. ever
104. really
105. Indian
     tent
106. sticks
107. paint
     everyone
108. . . . .
109. . . . .
110. chief
     whole
111. which
112. carrots
     hope
113. . . . .
114. rabbit
     truth
115. someone
116. even
117. first
     else
118. . . . .
120. ending
     hospital
121. . . . .
122. people
123. children
124. . . . .
125. keep
126. other
128. . . . .

UNIT 5

129. party
     George

     Laura
     Patsy
     Fred
130. . . . .
131. guess
132. game
     birthday
133. . . . .
134. . . . .
135. . . . .
136. . . . .
137. shoes
     dress
138. talking
139. yourself
140. giving
141. . . . .
142. . . . .
143. does
144. prize
     loser
145. fair
     maybe
146. touch
147. . . . .
148. . . . .
149. . . . .
150. . . . .
151. hurt
     us
152. galloped
153. ponies
154. . . . .
155. . . . .
156. . . . .
157. suppose
158. . . . .

UNIT 6

159. *Daniel*
     King
     Hoja
160. trusted
161. prays
     God
162. order
     lions
163. den
164. . . . .
165. . . . .
166. . . . .
167. wolf
     sheep
168. . . . .
169. joke
170. . . . .
171. . . . .
172. . . . .
173. . . . .
174. . . . .
175. . . . .
176. . . . .
177. . . . .
178. . . . .
179. . . . .
180. . . . .
181. garden
     grows
182. watermelon
     vines
183. tree
184. nut
185. . . . .
186. . . . .
187. . . . .

PICTURE DICTIONARY

At Play

Betsy   Jack   Susan   Tommy

At School

Anne   Bobby   Nancy

Peter   Pogo   Miss White

At Home

Betsy Anne   Carol   Danny

Jack   Peggy   Uncle Peter   Will

At Work

Miss Best

Bill

Davy

Dick

Jimmy

Julie

Paul

Tommy

Mr. Wills

At Party Time

Candy

Danny

Fred

George

Laura

Nancy May

Patsy

Peter

At Story Time

The Boy Who Cried Wolf

Daniel   Daniel's King   Hoja

The King Who Could Not Smile

A Beka Book Publications, an outgrowth of Pensacola Christian School, is a Christian ministry designed to meet the need for Christian textbooks and teaching aids for Christian schools. The purpose of this publications ministry is to help Christian schools reach children and young people for the Lord and train them in the Christian way of life.

If we can be of further help to your ministry, please write **A Beka Book Publications,** Box 18000, Pensacola, Florida 32523.